MW00614993

# 12 Secrets for Healing

# 12 Secrets
# for Healing

## Sacred Wisdom to Enhance the Healing Life

William E. Hablitzel, M.D.

Copyright 2008 William E. Hablitzel

Published in the United States by
Sunshine Ridge Publishing

Submit all requests for reprinting to:
Sunshine Ridge Publishing
4200 Sunshine Ridge Road
P.O. Box 69
Blue Creek, Ohio 45616
(888) 220-0397
info@Sunshine-Ridge.com

All rights reserved. No part of this publication may
be reproduced, stored in a retrieval system or trans-
mitted, in any form, or by any means, electronic,
mechanical, recorded, photocopied, or otherwise,
without the prior permission of the copyright
owner, except by a reviewer who may quote brief
passages in a review.

Library of Congress Control Number: 2008904147

ISBN: 978-0-9772185-3-0

# Contents

# Foreword

HAVE you ever read a book acclaimed as one of the greatest ever written, which had been read by millions and inspired many to greatness? Did you finish the book and ponder its message as simply common sense, but when the lessons learned were put into use incredible results appeared? Such is the case with Bill's new book, *12 Secrets for Healing.*

I remember being a high school student when I first heard the calling to become a physician. I went off to college with the desire to become a healer. I expected medical school to teach a systematic approach to healing and eagerly anticipated the *secrets* that learned doctors would share. Instead, I found millions of facts to memorize. I learned about diagnosis. I learned the traditions of Western medicine. I learned what medication to prescribe for a particular symptom. But I did not learn how to heal. To heal, I had to learn to tap into something that was already within me, something that

I was born with and something that you were born with as well. It is something that cannot be named, yet has miraculous power and potential. It is the source of all healing and so very simple to implement. To use it requires dedication and the desire to heal. The techniques are simple, perhaps too simple. That simplicity might explain why these lessons have been long overlooked, conceivably unworthy of being taught to young physicians. As I struggled with the teachings of medical school, I often confided my frustration and unsatisfied thirst to my friend and medical school advisor, Dr. William Hablitzel. He has written a wonderful book, a treasure of wisdom on healing—simple, yet profound.

The emergency room seems an unlikely place for healing, but yet, it is the place where I practice my trade, where rapid diagnosis and treatment is all consuming. In the emergency room heart attack victims seek life-saving intervention, asthmatics look for easier breaths, and the trauma patient just wants the hurt to go away—healing will come later. True emergencies however, are surprisingly infrequent among the dozens of patients who I see each day and I often find myself frustrated with the countless trivial problems that seem out-of-place among the urgent and important. Perhaps the man who has had back pain for many weeks, the elderly lady who feels tired all the time, or the college student who is unable to sleep seek more than treatment or even cure. Perhaps, they are looking for healing. It is an awareness that stirs the healer within, an empowering awareness that challenges one's perception of what is truly important.

The simplest gift can have the most profound effect. Once we pay attention to the circumstances around us, our consciousness expands, often to limits that we had never thought possible. There is great order within the universe and once we learn to embrace it, we can find a powerful message where once chaos seemed to reign. Not only does Bill recognize the message, his ability to share it with others through the written word is a precious gift. As you read the pages that follow and allow their lessons to become part of your life, your ability to heal will expand to profound limits. It is important to remember, however, that no matter what role you play in life, you have the opportunity to help heal. Some of the most powerful healers that I have come to know have never attended medical school. Look for healers in your life and become one. Bill will help you on your journey.

The lesson comes not only from the message, but through the awareness of how we come to find ourselves in just the right place at just the right time. There are no accidents in the universe. Think about the myriad events that had to perfectly align in order for you to be holding this book in your hands. Bill is one of my dearest teachers. I hope you are as thrilled to embark on this wonderful journey as I was to read—and read again—this life-changing book. Keep it close at hand and refer to it often. May the words and ideas soak into your soul—as they have mine—so that we may all know the peace of being healed as we help others find healing.

—Ken "Dusty" Mapes, M.D.
Emergency medicine physician and
author of *The ER Survival Guide*

# Introduction

A newspaper caught my eye as I walked through the waiting room at the end of the day, no doubt left there by one of my patients. It had been many years since I had subscribed to a newspaper or made its purchase part of my early-morning ritual. Picking it up from the coffee table, perhaps in curiosity or just with the novelty of holding it, I found myself pulled to another place, to another time some twenty years earlier.

The heavily starched collar of my lab coat rubbed annoyingly against my neck as I sat in the examination room. Its whiteness was pristine and its crispness spoke of newness. It was my first lab coat as a doctor and the fit seemed rather snug and strangely uncomfortable. I had been a doctor for only a few days, but already sat looking into the eyes of an expectant patient. The seventy-five-year-old lady was to be my first patient and I couldn't help but wonder if she knew the secret I closely guarded—I didn't know how to be a doctor.

Etta Mae Morris had a kind face, but I found little comfort in it. Her soft voice and gentle ways provided no sanctuary. Instead, I took refuge in the thick chart left to me by my predecessor. It would tell me all that I needed to know about my patient and the challenges that awaited me.

The internal medicine clinic was a great place for a resident physician. The patients from the underserved neighborhoods that surrounded the teaching hospital provided limitless opportunities to put the theories learned in medical school to practical use. I would spend three years as Etta Mae's doctor, just as my predecessor had and his predecessor had before him.

Like most clinics at urban teaching hospitals, management of chronic health problems consumed much of our time. Etta Mae's needs were overwhelming. Thumbing through her chart I learned that she had emphysema, diabetes, and hypertension. In each progress note her doctors expressed frustration with her continued smoking despite the severity of her emphysema. Her high blood sugar seemed impervious to frequent medication changes, dietary counseling, and urged exercise. It was her hypertension, however, that would seize my immediate attention.

After wrapping the blood pressure cuff around her arm, I watched in stunned horror as the mercury column fell.

Certain that the measurement was wrong, I repeated the process two more times before I was willing to accept the results, as impossible as they seemed to me.

"Mrs. Morris," I stated in a concerned, if not frightened, voice, "this is the highest blood pressure that I have ever seen. It's 230/120. Are you taking your medicine?"

"Oh," she replied matter-of-factly, "have you seen many blood pressures?"

The fact was that I hadn't, but it seemed irrelevant to all that I had studied and learned about blood pressure. My inexperience did nothing to mitigate the dangers I feared for my new patient, and I was confounded by her calmness. At the very least, she should have been as worried as I was, even if she didn't understand why.

The cure to my inexperience was found in her chart—I didn't have to work hard to come up with a solution for the first clinical problem I was to face as a doctor. Medication had been added previously for similar concerns, medication that I couldn't find among the bottles of pills that she had brought with her. With a smile, she took the prescription that I offered for the medication that had mysteriously vanished from her daily routine. I felt good. I had helped this old lady.

That good feeling lasted the better part of two weeks until Etta Mae returned to the clinic for her follow-up visit.

I was certain that her blood pressure would be better, but it wasn't.

"Your blood pressure is still high, Mrs. Morris. Are you taking the new medicine I gave you?" I asked with concern.

"Don't look so worried, Doctor," she replied reassuringly. "I'm doing just fine."

"But are you taking your medicine?" I pressed.

"Of course, I am," she said softly.

I wrote Etta Mae a new prescription, doubling the strength of the medication I had started earlier. Two weeks later, her blood pressure remained elevated, and I added an additional medication to her list. I saw Etta Mae every two weeks, and every two weeks she remained refractory to my efforts. My frustration grew with every visit. Not only was I not helping her blood pressure, I hadn't even started to work on her emphysema. The chart told me that her emphysema was severe, yet she continued to smoke two packs of cigarettes every day. As far as her diabetes went, I had seen maple syrup with lower levels of sugar than that which coursed through Etta Mae's veins. I was losing the battle without ever recognizing the enemy.

After months of aggravation, I again asked Etta Mae to bring all of her medications to her next appointment. Her smile never wavered as I sorted through the bottles of pills that she had emptied from her purse. Not one of the medications that I had prescribed was among them. A call to her pharmacy confirmed my suspicions—she had never had my prescriptions filled. I was more stunned than I was angry. For the better part of a year, I had accomplished nothing.

"Why, Mrs. Morris?" I asked in disbelief. "Why haven't you taken any of the medicine that I prescribed?"

"I didn't need them, Doctor," she said softly. "I am doing just fine with what I have. I didn't need any more."

"Mrs. Morris, I've been working hard to help you. You are seriously ill, and I'm worried about you. You are going to have a stroke with this blood pressure so high."

"I'm not going to have a stroke," she said emphatically. "I don't do strokes."

"And what about those cigarettes?" I challenged, clearly in a mood to vent months of building frustration. "Your lungs are horrible; the smoking is going to kill you."

"You don't know that," she said, calmly. "I know my body better than you do and what it needs and doesn't need."

"I do know that, Mrs. Morris," I argued. "We have studies and experience with such things. If you don't start taking better care of yourself, you are not going to live much longer."

"Now, Bill," she gently scolded, "don't take yourself too

seriously. Nobody knows such things, and all of the pills in the world are not going to change what is to be."

It was the first time that a patient had ever addressed me by my first name, and it startled me a bit. But it seemed strangely appropriate. She wasn't speaking to the doctor but to the soul that, perhaps, had become lost inside.

"Etta Mae," I asked softly, "why do you come here if you won't let me help you?

"I come to see you," she explained simply, "and it does help me—very much so."

"Then why do you take the prescriptions when you have no intention of getting them filled?" I asked.

"Because it makes you feel good," she said, peering intently into my eyes. "And that makes me feel good."

The memory was a vivid one, one that had found a special place to rest deep within my soul. I studied the picture of Etta Mae in the newspaper that I held in my hand. It was just as I had remembered her. Her obituary brought a broad smile to my face. The lady whose imminent demise I once predicted had lived to the age of ninety-five. She had been one of my teachers. I wondered how many other doctors she had helped train—to reflect upon the possibility that cure just isn't enough.

Much of my life has been spent in training, preparing for a future life. The fire academy honed skills buried deep within me that once found, I never wanted to use. Medical school taught me all about cure. Residency taught me how to make that cure possible.

When I completed my residency, I was a highly skilled physician. I found comfort among the sickest of patients and faced emergency with calmness. I could keep a table alive in the intensive care unit overnight if I had to, but I knew little about back pain, sore throats, rash, or the most common complaint, "Doctor, I just don't feel well." I knew nothing of healing.

Those important things I had to learn from my greatest of teachers—my patients.

Physicians are invited deep into the lives of their patients. People will tell their doctors secrets hidden from family and their closest of friends. That willingness to share combined with the circumstances that move people to seek out their physicians—illness, injury, tragedy, sadness, or even death—sets a magical stage upon which the dance of life is performed. These are command performances in which few are privileged to watch. If we seize the opportunity and watch closely, incredible secrets of life are ours for the taking. They are secrets that can help us discover meaning and happiness, secrets that can make ordinary life extraordinary, and secrets that can teach us how to heal.

There is an ancient Buddhist proverb that says, "When the student is ready, the teacher will appear." Sometimes, our teachers appear before we are ready or willing to learn the lessons they offer. They wait patiently in our thoughts and memories until the time is right to learn. Etta Mae was one such teacher.

If you are ready, special teachers wait for you in the pages that follow. They have been my patients, sacred friends who have left behind astonishing secrets. While their names and circumstances have been changed, their stories are true and the secrets that they share are precious gifts. They are secrets that can change your life and turn a life of caring into one of healing. The journey will be extraordinary.

—William E. Hablitzel, M.D.

*Your heart knows in silence the secrets of the days and the nights.*

—Kahlil Gibran

*When I stand before thee at the day's end, thou shalt see my scars and know that I had my wounds and also my healing.*

—Rabindranath Tagore

*The First Secret*

# Start Your Day in Silence

WHEN I first met Hazel, it was as if I had known her for a long time. We had started our days together for several years, although she wasn't aware of it. The paths of our morning rituals crossed just outside of the medical school cafeteria. My path led to coffee and an occasional bagel—sustenance that would carry me through the morning's first lecture. Mornings in medical school always seemed to arrive after too little sleep and with an awareness that I had too much to do.

My morning routine was planned to the minute—ten minutes for a shower, three minutes to clean the windshield, and ninety seconds to make it through that interminably slow traffic light on the edge of town—in order to squeeze every precious drop of sleep from the all too brief night. I would arrive at the medical school with just enough time to stop by the cafeteria, fill my coffee mug, and be in my seat in the large lecture hall that was my home for the first two years of training.

You notice everything when you're in a new place, particularly when you're uncertain of the journey to come. From the harsh sterile lighting to the cafeteria's hideous mauve wall coverings, no detail was too small to escape notice in those early days. Not far from the cafeteria, along the corridor that took me, with coffee in hand, to the lecture halls, was a small waiting area partly shielded by lush ivy, ferns, and palms. It was a quiet, seemingly forgotten place with a few comfortable chairs that didn't fit in the utilitarian world of a teaching hospital.

In one of those chairs was a middle-aged woman. She sat erect with her feet flat on the floor and hands gently resting in her lap. Her closed eyes conveyed a sense of peace. It seemed a strange time for a nap, but then again, my day was just starting and sleep would have come easily. When I saw her on the second day and then again on the third day, I began to suspect that this was more than just a tired lady.

As days stretched into weeks and weeks into months, each morning began with a trip to the cafeteria for coffee. With every trip she was there—sitting in the same chair, in the same position, and with the same look of peace that I had observed earlier. I found myself stepping quietly as I passed, careful not to intrude upon what seemed almost a spiritual experience, one that I didn't fully understand.

In those first two years of medical school, there wasn't a morning that I didn't see her. Although we had never met or made eye contact, I came to regard her as a friend and would have missed her if she hadn't been there each morning. With the third year of medical school, daily routine would change as education moved from the lecture hall to the hospital.

Mornings still started with coffee, but not with a trip to the cafeteria and a fleeting moment with my friend.

The hospital was the antithesis of the lecture hall's order and tranquility, a transition that took some getting used to. Everyone—doctors, nurses, aides, and particularly the house staff—seemed harried and challenged. No place was this more evident than in the emergency room. It was a stressful place for medical students—where the desire to help was overwhelmed by the reality that their skills could do little to alter the pain and suffering that they encountered there.

The most difficult job in the emergency room didn't belong to the doctors, although they would dispute this assertion. It didn't belong to the nurses. The most difficult job belonged to the unit clerk. Doctors made the decisions, but it was the unit clerk who found a way to make it happen. They were always in the middle of every problem but in the periphery of every success. It was a stressful job that was visibly apparent on even the most tranquil of hospital floors. Unit clerks had the power to make medical students' lives difficult, and a student's success, or at least their sanity, was often dependent on the clerk's mood. I wasn't looking forward to my rotation in the emergency room.

My first impression of the emergency room was one of chaos. Shouted orders, patients' screams, the rattling of carts, and the beeping of monitors contributed to a deafening cacophony that I can still hear to this day. Telephones rang continuously from the central desk, the department's command center. Patients lined the front of the desk while doctors and nurses assaulted the back, each vying for the attention of the sole unit clerk.

I was struck by the unit clerk, a middle-aged woman who had a touch of gray in her hair. If she was stressed she didn't show it. In fact, she was smiling. Her movements were deliberate and portrayed nothing but confidence and calm. She seemed to know just what issues required immediate attention and how to bring comfort to those that had to wait. As I watched her, I was shocked with a sudden epiphany. She was my friend who had sat outside the cafeteria every morning.

This lady fascinated me. I was eager to learn more about her, but the emergency room's frenetic pace seldom provided more than fleeting moments in which to talk. In a span of a deep breath or two, she could explain a long wait to an angry patient, assure an impatient doctor that the laboratory results were on their way, and offer a colorful sticker to a frightened child. She was the eye of a hurricane—an island of calm in the midst of a great storm. Even great storms grow quiet, but the emergency room never did, and she was always there.

Over the course of my month's assignment, each brief chat provided another piece of the puzzle to understanding her. Her name was Hazel, and she had worked in the emergency room for more than fifteen years, an unprecedented tenure in such a high-pressured job. I once asked her how she remained so calm when everybody wanted something from her at the same time.

"I wasn't always calm," she answered. "At least, I didn't look too calm."

"Well, you do now, Hazel," I said. "What happened?"

"For years I felt like a rat on a treadmill," she replied, "running constantly but accomplishing nothing. I came to work dreading what was to come and left at the end of the day feeling exhausted. What came in between was just a job, not the satisfaction that I was looking for when I started working here. There were all of these people to help, but you can't help people when all of your thoughts are focused on how rushed you are and how bad you feel."

"So what did you do?" I asked.

"I found silence," she said softly. "On my days off I went to the park, took a long walk, or just sat in my backyard for hours. I always felt a sense of peace there, and the feeling stayed with me for the rest of the day. But there was more. In the quiet of those places, I heard a soft voice, and it came from within. Although I didn't understand how, I knew that voice spoke to me, so I started to listen. Life seemed so clear on those days—a clarity that I had never found at work.

"My car was in the shop one morning, so I had to take the bus to work. It got me here almost an hour early. I wasn't about to walk into this place a minute before I had to, so I got myself a cup of tea and found a place to wait. It was a quiet place, and I started to feel that wonderful peace that had visited me in the park. As I sat in the quiet I could hear that soft voice, and the voice spoke to me. Work wasn't the same that day, and it hasn't been the same since. Now, I start my day in silence."

It was some time before I was ready to learn the lesson that Hazel had left with me. It started with a telephone call from a friend as I was getting ready for work one morning. Perhaps sprouting from seeds that I had planted during my days in medical school, my mornings were tightly regimented and always short on time. I loathed surprises—anything that took me off schedule. Whether it was a snow-covered driveway, a malfunctioning coffee pot, or that telephone call from a friend, the end result was always the same: I was going to be late for work, and that made me crazy.

Typical of most days, Talk radio accompanied me on my commute. Having awakened to the radio and listened to it while showering and dressing, there wasn't anything that I particularly wanted to hear, but I was accustomed to the background noise. On days that I was running late and feeling stressed, however, talk radio always provided me with something to be angry about. It was how I started my day—late, frustrated, and angry.

My first patient of the morning was new to me. She

dismissed my apologies for being late and charmed me with her smile. She was a young lady and needed a physical examination before starting a new job. The job excited her, and she was looking forward to the opportunity to help people. She was going to be a clerk in the emergency room. She asked me if I had any tips that might help her.

"Just one," I said. "Start your day in silence."

Whatever your work—as a plumber, teacher, grocer, nurse, or even physician—it is hard to give your best when feeling stressed. The treadmill of our daily lives runs so fast, our resources have been drawn so thin, and the environment around us has become so chaotic that, more often than not, we are oblivious to the tension that consumes our days. Perhaps we have grown so accustomed to the turmoil that we would miss it if it were to disappear, like the radio always playing in the background.

By starting our day in silence, we take responsibility for how we feel and what we can accomplish. Rather than spending the day reacting to the events around us, we choose to create the events that best serve our purpose. For me, this means getting up a little earlier every morning and making time for quiet part of my daily routine. The television stays off, and I have banished talk radio from my commute. Now, I spend the first ten minutes of my workday alone in my office. The lights are low as I sit back in my chair with closed eyes. In the silence I hear that voice Hazel spoke of and feel the calm that it brings. It is the start of a special day and with it comes the opportunity for more than treatment and cure. From the silence comes the potential to heal.

# Simple Steps for Putting the First Secret to Work

- Create time every morning that you can spend in silence. Get up a little earlier, postpone some daily chores, or perhaps give up the morning newspaper.

- Reduce the noise in your morning. Wake to quiet music rather than a harsh alarm. Don't turn on the television. Shun the radio.

- Make your commute to work in silence. Stay off of the cell phone. Turn off the radio. If you must have it on, try listening to soft music rather than the news or talk programming.

- Find your special place of quiet. You can have more than one—one at home and one at work. It should be a place where you can be alone and be undisturbed. It should be a comfortable place—a favorite chair in the study, the backyard porch, or a seldom-used conference room at the office. If possible, things of beauty—a potted plant, an aquarium, or items of art—should be nearby.

- Turn off the phone or send callers to voicemail. This is your special time to be alone.

- Sit, relax, close your eyes, and enjoy the silence. Notice the thoughts that come and go, and focus on whatever seems appropriate. Start out with ten minutes every day, and gradually increase to thirty minutes or more. If it is difficult at first, be patient. It will get easier.

- Sit in silence every day, even if only for five minutes. It takes three weeks to establish a habit, and this is one habit well worth starting.

*It is the province of knowledge to speak, it is the privilege of wisdom to listen.*

—Oliver Wendell Holmes

*We only consult the ear because the heart is wanting.*

—Blaise Pascal

*A person hears only what they understand.*

—Johann Wolfgang von Goethe

*The Second Secret*

# Listening

MY most important tool in medicine was never discussed in medical school. It was ignored in residency. Perhaps, it is too simplistic for scholarly discussions or not complicated enough to join the traditions of medicine. My most important tool in medicine is *listening*.

For all its pomp and circumstance, medicine is a rather simple profession. Ninety-five percent of patients, if we ask the right questions, will tell us what is wrong them. Most will tell us what needs to be done to help them. All we have to do is *listen*. How simple is that?

In the hills of Appalachia in rural southern Ohio, there is a place of great beauty and tranquility. It is there that I best hear the wisdom that can be found in silence. It is a poor county with great need, and it has become the site of a free medical clinic at the local health department where I have been blessed with the opportunity to serve. With little money for tests or medications, the power of listening is palpable. Through that listening the special teachers of that place have shared a great secret—listening is more than a tool that can lead to cure, it can heal.

David Drask didn't have a doctor and he was referred to the clinic by the emergency room of the local hospital. He was a young man, only eighteen years old, but was already on his own. He was tall and thin and wore clothes that probably hadn't fit him well for some time and were in need of mending. He was shy and had gentle ways, and I liked him immediately. Thrust into the responsibilities of adulthood before his time, his eyes had darkness where a sparkle should have been. I wondered how much of his youth had been lost.

David had been raised on a small piece of land about twelve miles outside of town that had been left to his father by a great uncle. It was poor land, both hilly and rocky, but his father tried his best to farm it. Even tobacco struggled to grow there. Suspicious of the outside world, his mother had home-schooled David and he had grown up without friends. A year earlier, or perhaps two, his parents had moved on in search of a better life, leaving David behind to care for the few animals that they had had. They had said they would send for him once they had settled, but word had never come.

The emergency room's report revealed that David had been seen for finger pain, was diagnosed with a minor sprain, and had been sent home with samples of an anti-inflammatory medication. It seemed an unusual reason to visit the hospital, particularly for such an independent young man. More curious, however, was the notation that it had been his sixth visit to the emergency room in just a couple of months. A call to the hospital confirmed earlier visits for a rash, a headache, back pain, indigestion, and a sore throat. He had become a familiar figure to the emergency room staff. Often, he waited for hours for a visit with the physician that seldom required more than a minute or two.

Other than being somewhat underweight, David appeared to be in good health. Because he had been home-schooled, he had missed the typical safeguards that ensured adequate immunizations, but it was something that could be remedied at the health department. David seemed embarrassed and rather surprised by the interest in him but nonetheless politely answered questions that probed uncomfortably into his life. He didn't have any bills and was able to get by with occasional odd jobs, although he admitted that it was getting harder to find enough work in the country. He didn't have a car, and didn't even know how to drive for that matter, but got around on old bicycle.

"How did you get to the hospital the other day?" I asked.

"I rode my bike," he replied as if the answer was too obvious to speak.

Peering into those eyes I was touched by their darkness. There was a secret there—one a man wanted to keep but one that a boy needed to share.

"You rode your bike halfway across the county and back again for a sore finger?" I asked. "I don't believe it David.

And what about all of those other visits? It's hard to picture you going to a doctor for such minor stuff."

His eyes widened in surprise, or perhaps, in relief.

"My finger was hurting a whole lot worse before I got there," he said.

"David," I prodded softly, "why did you go?"

With a deep sigh, he started his story.

"Everyone out by us always goes to the hospital when they don't feel good or when they need something. But, gee, you just can't show up without a good reason," he said.

"So David," I urged, "why did you go?"

"I've never been scared before," he said, "at least, not like this. I don't have any money, and there's not any more work to do near home. I've done everything that people will pay me for. I was hoping the doctor would give me medicine, so I wouldn't feel scared all of the time. I was even going to ask if the hospital had any work that I could do."

"So what happened?" I asked.

"Heck," David said, "I could have counted to ten in the time that it took the doc to look at my hand and move my fingers around. He never even spoke to me. Just said something to the nurse who was with him."

"And what now, David?" I asked softly.

"I'm still scared," he said is a whisper, obviously embarrassed as a tear rolled from his eye. "I don't have anything to feed Abbey today. All I had to give her yesterday was half of a ham sandwich."

"Who's Abbey?" I asked.

"She's my dog," he replied with a grin.

It was the first time I had seen him smile, even if it was fleeting.

"David, when was the last time you had something to eat?" I asked

He glanced at me briefly before looking away and sat in silence a full minute before answering in a hushed voice, "It's been a couple of days."

His words left me stunned.

"You mean you gave your dog your only food yesterday?" I asked.

"Sure," he said. "We take care of each other. I'm all she has."

Seldom have I encountered words that touched so deeply, inspired so thoroughly, or taught so completely— words that could have far too easily passed unheard.

The ticket to admission to our health-care system is often a symptom or a problem. Medical students are taught that sixty percent of visits to a primary care provider have a psychosocial cause as the basis of their presenting symptom or complaint. It is a statistic that always gives me pause, particularly on busy days when the schedule is filled with the casualties of life. How many patients leave their physician's office unhealed—depression disguised as fatigue, loneliness masquerading as gastritis, grief cloaked in chest pain, or disappointment hidden in back pain—for lack of a listening ear?

David left the clinic that day with a gift certificate to a local grocery, not as a gift but as payment for future chores and odd jobs. Referrals to social services helped provide the essentials of life while a job and hard work did the rest. David still comes to the clinic but seldom with a problem. Now, he comes just to talk, and as we listen, we have the opportunity to heal.

# Simple Steps for Putting the Second Secret to Work

- The simple act of listening is healing. It doesn't have to happen in a clinical setting. Listening can happen anywhere and for anyone.

- There is a difference between *hearing* and *listening*. Hearing only requires our presence. Listening demands our intention.

- Look for opportunities to listen in your personal life—the friend who telephones unexpectedly, the preoccupied spouse who insists that nothing is wrong, or the coworker who stops smiling. Not only will it hone your listening skills, but it also will enrich your life.

- Be vigilant for those who have a hunger to be listened to—the visit without clear reason, the persistent problem that defies explanation or resolution, those who seem to travel through life alone, or the individual who makes you feel sad.

- End every encounter with a question and the time for an answer—is there anything that you want me to know?

*Nothing valuable can be lost by taking time.*

—Abraham Lincoln

*Much may be done in those little shreds and patches of time which every day produces, and which most men throw away.*

—Charles Caleb Colton

*The Third Secret*

# Taking Time

ONE of the first things that I learned in medical school was that time was my enemy. I would never have enough. Time was measured in units that spanned from one examination to the next and its value vested, not in the experience, but in the number of pages read, laboratories completed, and lectures attended. Time was a precious commodity to be invested wisely—never to be given away.

Residency provided the battleground upon which I refined my skills of combat against time. I learned to accept the premise that there would never be enough time. Eating quickly, sleeping less, writing hastily, and walking briskly all became tools to help squeeze every morsel of productivity from each fleeting moment. Often, patients became obstacles to managing the day. The added patient in clinic was not an opportunity to serve but another reason for a cold dinner. The late-night admission offered not a chance to learn but the loss of precious sleep.

It was with these memories that I smiled when a patient recently said to me, "Doctor, that specialist you sent me to never took his hand off of the doorknob during my entire visit."

We learned our lessons well and far too many of us

practice them to perfection. Those days taught me that curing could be quick work. It would be my greatest teachers—my patients—that would teach me that healing takes time.

Perhaps like a demon from my past, I still battle with time. When the office schedule is busy, the battles are pitched, and I lose more often than I win. My greatest challenge is running late—there is nothing that disturbs me and by extension, my staff more. We try hard to honor our patients' time by scheduling longer appointments for those with greater needs and scattering patients with simple problems throughout the day to help me catch up. Despite our best intentions, however, I inevitably run late.

Such was the case one morning not many years ago. I had stopped to see a sick patient at the hospital and was late getting to the office. My hopes of catching up faded with each patient I saw. By midmorning the waiting room was packed and I was feeling quite stressed about making my patients wait. But there was no mercy—Mrs. Shelby sat in the next room, and she had a list.

Nothing instills more dread in a busy doctor than an elderly lady with a list. I had followed Minnie Shelby for many years and liked her a lot, but she was a talker—a very slow talker. The list was endless and included such threats to happiness as the bitter taste of her blood pressure medicine, the intestinal gas she had after eating cucumbers, her cold feet at night, and raspberry seeds getting lodged under her dentures. Although chafing with every spent minute, I just couldn't rush this lady. It was the first time I had ever seen her in the office alone. She always had come with her husband, Joe, and the three of us always found something to laugh about. Joe died some six months earlier of pancreatic cancer. I was grateful that we had honored his wish to die at home and that she could be at his side, but I felt sorry for her loss, a loss which we did not speak of that day. Although hopelessly behind schedule, I felt somehow fulfilled when she managed a laugh after I suggested hospitalization for the raspberry seeds.

My battle with time was interrupted a week later by a letter that came in the afternoon mail. Obviously penned by an old and trembling hand, it was as difficult to read as it must have been to write.

*Dear Doctor,*

*Thank you for spending time with me today, even though you did not have it to give. I wanted you to know how much it meant to me. When Joe passed, my life went with him. I didn't think I could go on—I didn't want to go on. He was in horrible pain at the end and had powerful medicine for it. I never threw it away. The ability to drift off to sleep seemed a precious gift when compared to a life without Joe.*

*I laughed today. I had forgotten what it was like. I realized that Joe was still with me and always would be. I came straight home and threw away the pills.*

*Thank you for your gift of time, and life.*

*Minnie*

I've never thought of time in quite the same way after reading that letter. Sure, I'm often harried and running late, but time is no longer the enemy. It is the currency of the universe and our only true possession. We spend a lifetime accumulating things—job titles, property, and money—but it's all just stuff, stuff that will fade from existence when we leave this reality. What we exchange our time for defines our lives.

As I struggled with time, I was oblivious to its power of healing. Minnie's life was influenced not by the strength of a medication, the sophistication of a test, or the accuracy of a diagnosis. She was moved by the presence of her doctor, and in that presence, she found healing. It is healing that can not be explained by the scientific method. Perhaps, it is just too simple for that. Or maybe, it is much too complicated for our science to understand.

It is a tool that I do not need to understand to use, and I use it regularly. When tempted to rush from a patient's side, I think of Minnie and give a few minutes more. The minutes are spent not in diagnosis or treatment, but in anything that my patient may desire—a story, a joke, or perhaps a quiet moment together—and in those minutes, there is healing.

# Simple Steps for Putting the Third Secret to Work

- Look for an opportunity to give of yourself through time every day—take in a ballgame with the kids, go on a walk with a friend, or visit the elderly lady next door. It sharpens the habit of healing.

- Every telephone call returned offers the chance to give part of your day to others. Turn a task into an opportunity to help heal.

- Time spent in active attention is perceived as longer and of greater value than that shared with other activities. Avoid taking notes when with others—it dilutes the power of your presence.

- Never look at your watch—it minimizes your gift of time.

- Practice giving one minute more at the end of each encounter.

Let your best be for your friend...

—Kahlil Gibran

The glory of friendship is not in the outstretched hand, nor the kindly smile, nor the joy of companionship; it is in the spiritual inspiration that comes to one when he discovers that someone else believes in him and is willing to trust him.

—Ralph Waldo Emerson

*The Fourth Secret*

# Treat Everyone You Meet as Though They Were Friend or Family

SOMEWHERE from my earliest moments of training came the admonishment—doctors must never treat friends or family. Perhaps, the closeness of such relationships prevented the professional detachment that seemed so important to our teachers. Maybe, too great an interest in the outcome might influence judgment. Possibly, it protected us from the emotional trauma of an adverse ending. Like most of the doctrines of medicine that were passed down to us, it wasn't important that we understood, only that we carried them with us into another time. They were lessons of cure but not of healing. Those important lessons would have to wait for special teachers.

Those teachers of healing began appearing the minute I became a doctor. Often, I was too busy to notice, or perhaps, too insecure in my new profession to listen. One special teacher was Roger Harold. I had been a doctor for only a few weeks when I first met Roger, and I found great comfort in the realization that the theories from medical school worked. His symptoms and clinical examinations made for an easy diagnosis, and even the most inexperienced of physicians could bring him comfort.

In the weeks that I cared for Roger, we developed a closeness that, perhaps, my earliest teachers would have found best to avoid. Somewhere amid the daily exams, the drawing of blood, and the trips back and forth to radiology, Roger became more than an *interesting case* on morning rounds or a daily entry in the medical record. His story and thoughts became as important as the laboratory results and exam findings that I had learned about in school—perhaps, more important. It was a subtle recognition that was more like the planting of a seed, which one day would grow and bear fruit.

My teachers from medical school had filled me with vast knowledge about life and illness but little of its wisdom. That there was more to learn was as great a revelation as the realization that not all of our patients would find cure. I had experienced death before. As a paramedic, it was dramatic, sometimes dreadful, and always much too frequent. I had never encountered death, however, as intimately as it visited Roger and me. It was more than an event—it was a journey.

It was a sad day when I sat with Roger to tell him what he already knew—that his illness was beyond medicine's power to cure. He offered an invitation too rare to refuse—to walk the journey with him. He offered counsel too extraordinary to ignore—treat me as if I were your father. It was a secret that would change the way I practice medicine.

There can be no greater compliment than to have a friend refer a patient to your care. But it can come with some anxiety—the desire not to disappoint and the need to prove worthy of his trust and confidence. But when that patient is also a friend, the apprehension can be almost overpowering. Such was the case when I walked into my exam room one day to find Ed waiting.

Ed was the father of my closest friend. Actually, Ryan and I were more than friends. Starting internship together, we experienced the best and the worst that a busy teaching hospital has to offer. We learned how to care for the sickest of patients, we honed clinical skills to a keen edge, and we felt the exhilaration of cure and the sadness of death—and we did it together. His family became my family. Through Sunday evening dinners, Christmas mornings with children, and the treasured honor as the godfather to his second daughter, he enriched my life with wonders that might have otherwise gone unknown.

Ed was a few years older than my own father was, and, in fact, his gentle ways, kind heart, and seasoned wisdom reminded me of the man back home whom I seldom had a chance to see. I couldn't possibly be Ed's doctor. I wasn't good enough. What if something went wrong?

One afternoon, I received the telephone call that I had waited for with dread. Ed had passed out in church. Ed had been my patient for a number of years, and while I never grew comfortable as his physician, I reluctantly surrendered to the responsibility that both honored and frightened me.

I watched Ed like a hawk—studying every medication for adverse reactions, guarding him from the tunnel vision of his specialists, and watching for the slightest abnormalities in his laboratory studies.

In the emergency room, Ed appeared his normal self. Nothing in his examination, in his labs, or on his EKG gave me cause for worry, but then again, this was Ed, and nothing explained why he had suddenly lost consciousness. Despite his pleas to go home and over his strong objections, I had him admitted to the hospital for observation.

When I looked in on Ed in the coronary care unit, he was more concerned about missing his golf game the following morning than anything that might be wrong with his heart. I would have been worried had he not been concerned about missing golf. Sitting in the nursing station writing my admission note, I glanced across the thirty-some feet into my patient's room. Startled, I took a second look. The face that had been smiling at me just minutes before was now colored a deep blue. A frantic look at the monitor over his bed revealed no blood pressure, no heart rate, and a rhythm of ventricular fibrillation. Ed was dead.

The CCU sprung into dance. It was choreography of the highest degree; a well-rehearsed, yet seldom-used spectacular that could restore potential to lifeless forms. CPR was started, medications administered, and electrical shocks delivered. In a matter of minutes, a normal rhythm returned to his EKG, a blood pressure appeared on the monitor, and life returned to Ed's face. He was confused by the activity that had appeared around his bed and more than a little amused with the concerned faces that peered down at him. The moments that Ed had spent in darkness, however, had turned the seemingly trivial event at church into a huge concern.

Ed would need a cardiac catheterization and he would need it immediately. The interventional cardiologist who had responded to the emergency and had led the resuscitation team agreed. Unfortunately, he was the only cardiologist available. Regrettably, the duty would fall to my friend Ryan.

I watched the procedure from the anteroom of the cardiac catheterization laboratory. Despite having looked down at the lifeless form of his father only an hour before, the calmness in Ryan's voice and the steadiness of his hand amazed me. The cath lab staff seemed stunned by Ryan's speed and expertise as they gathered around to watch the ordinary become extraordinary. The physician spoke to his patient with words of knowledge and skill while the son spoke to his father with compassion and love. It was a powerful blend that touched me deeply. Perhaps, for the very first time, I was aware of the power of healing.

Ed's disease was far more extensive than what could be treated in the catheterization laboratory, and within hours he was in the operating room for emergency bypass surgery. Many years have passed since that day and Ed still plays golf, beating men half his age. Throughout those years, I have watched a special closeness between father and son, perhaps, a closeness that is only possible when we bring healing into our lives.

Friends bring out the best in us. Often, they know far better than we do the potential that resides within our lives, and they stick with us until that potential becomes reality. There is energy to friendship, an energy that makes us feel good just by being in someone's presence. It is a healing energy. Imagine bringing that energy into the lives of others, whether it be a patient, a neighbor, or the boss at work.

When the treadmill runs particularly fast and I question my capacity to give, I find myself thinking back to the secret that Roger shared and Ryan put to use. I no longer dread caring for a friend and try to approach each of my patients as one. They help me find my best and to experience the magic that I had long sought in medicine. By treating each of my patients as friends, I have discovered that it does not take long for them to become friends. But they have become much more—they have become my family.

# Simple Steps for Putting
# the Fourth Secret to Work

- Close your eyes and think for a moment about your best friend. How do you feel in his presence? How do you act in his presence? Is it different than when you are with a stranger or a business associate? Those feelings and behaviors are a reflection of the authentic you—remember them throughout your day.

- Think about a family member who is particularly close to you, perhaps a mother or a sister. Imagine her meeting a person with the potential to help her, not in a small way, but in a way that could change her life. If you could select one characteristic that this person would have, what would it be?

- Once each day, be that characteristic to a coworker, an acquaintance, or a perfect stranger.

- Before your next encounter with another soul, whether they are a patient, a client, or a lady from church—imagine that encounter as though it was with your best friend. Relax and let those authentic feelings and behaviors take over. It will make the ordinary extraordinary.

But O for the touch of a vanished hand, And the sound of a voice that is still.

—Lord Alfred Tennyson

He who would do good to another must do it in minute particulars …

—William Blake

*The Fifth Secret*

# There Is Power in Touch

**T**HERE are times in medicine when nothing more can be done. Grasping Phil's hand, I realized that this was one of those moments. His hand was cold and the fluids its tissues retained gave it a spongy texture. It was so much different from the first time I had grasped that hand—then in greeting—almost a year earlier.

His two daughters had accompanied, or perhaps, escorted him to my office. They had been determined that their father would take good care of himself after his recent diagnosis with diabetes. Phil had groused about their intrusion into his life, but it had been obvious that he was quite proud of them and had appreciated their concern. Actually, they made taking care of Phil a snap. It was guaranteed that Phil would follow any suggestion I made to one of them.

Phil had been experiencing fatigue for many months and began carrying a bottle of water with him wherever he went. Although he had denied it, his family was certain that he was losing weight. When he scheduled an appointment with the optometrist, his daughters, armed with their research from the Internet, were convinced that he was diabetic. A trip to Urgent Care confirmed their suspicions and brought the three of them to me.

It didn't take long for Phil to be a favorite face in the

office. He was one of those people who you just felt good being around. He knew each of my employees' names and asked each about their lives away from work. It was no wonder that he was a successful businessman, but then again, it was hard to picture Phil driving a hard bargain. Phil seemed to know and like everyone. It was not unusual for him to encounter a long long-lost friend sitting in the waiting room. Once I referred him to an ophthalmologist for diabetic eye care, only to discover that Phil had taught him baseball when he was a child.

Other than an impressively high triglyceride level in his blood, Phil's diabetes was his only health problem, one which quickly came under control with medication. So, too, did the triglycerides, although the low-fat diet challenged him to the fiber of his being. With every visit I learned a bit more about this man, and the more I learned, the more I liked him. Somewhere during the journey, he became my friend.

Very late one night, a call from the emergency room awakened me.

"I have Phil Grossmann here," the ER physician told me. "Is he a drinker?"

"No," I replied, instantly awake after hearing Phil's name. "Why do you ask?"

"He has pancreatitis," the doc told me, "and it's bad. His amylase is over 20,000."

"I don't think he drinks even socially," I said, "but his triglycerides are high. Maybe that's the problem."

There was little I could do that wasn't already being done, but I didn't hesitate a moment about getting out of bed and driving to the hospital. I was shocked when I saw Phil in the emergency room. Indeed, he looked bad. Although he did not respond to questions, he moaned and grasped at his abdomen as if in severe pain. The pallor of illness covered him like a blanket. Despite two intravenous lines rapidly infusing saline into his arms, his blood pressure was low and heart rate rapid.

His daughters were at his bedside, looking both surprised by his rapid decline and horrified by his appearance. They both had seen him earlier in the day, and he had looked fine. It wasn't until after dinner that he had begun to have some stomach discomfort, which was not the occasional indigestion he experienced when he ate too much. They had wanted to call me, but Phil didn't let them. He told them, I worked too hard and needed my evenings at home in peace. He assured them that he would be better by morning, and if not, he would call me then. But Phil didn't make it to the morning. His pain progressively increased, and within a few hours, he had slipped into unconsciousness.

Three days later, Phil was still in the intensive care unit. As I held that cold hand, I counted the IV controllers that circled the head of his bed, like wolves studying their prey.

There were six of them, and with the blink of a light, each dispensed a drop of medication into his circulation. Some of those medicines supported his blood pressure, which had fallen dangerously low in the emergency room. Pacemaker wires that disappeared into blood vessels in his neck regulated his heart, which had stopped twice before. A ventilator breathed for Phil, and if not for its metronome-like whirl, time seemed to stand still.

It was called necrotizing pancreatitis. Instead of digesting food, Phil's digestive enzymes had turned against their host and were slowly consuming him. His lungs were the first to fail and then came his heart. The kidneys were the next to go. One by one, organ systems failed, and we enlisted more consultants in the battle. Cardiologists, pulmonologists, gastroenterologists, nephrologists, and even neurologists saw Phil several times each day. I would have called an auto mechanic if I had thought it would help. As each of his specialists depleted their bag of tricks, Phil teetered on the edge of death.

There was nothing more to do, except wait. I wasn't very good at waiting. It wasn't something taught in medical school. What was taught, however, didn't seem to be making much of a difference. If Phil was to get better, it would not come from the medicine I knew so well, it would come from another place.

And better he got. At first, his improvement was

subtle—a slight rise in blood pressure, the return of a regular cardiac rhythm, and laboratory studies slowly drifting towards normal—and easy for the specialists to dismiss as wishful thinking. But in the days that followed, Phil came off of the ventilator, his blood pressure no longer needed to be supported by medication, his kidney function was returning, and there could be no doubt that he was indeed improving.

A week later, Phil was back. One morning during my rounds, I found him sitting up in bed, complaining about the sugar-free syrup for his pancakes, but his smile was as rich as the first day that I had met him. He was very much at peace, and his eyes contained a depth that I hadn't noticed before. There was a wisdom about him, a wisdom that I felt he wanted to share but didn't know how.

"How much do you remember?" I asked.

"I remember everything," he said in a clear voice. "Not so much the words, but the presence of all of the doctors and nurses, what they did to me, and most important, what they were feeling. Everyone thought I was going to die, and I thought so, too. I was so close to giving up."

I had never heard Phil speak in such a way. There was almost a reverence in his voice. Perhaps, it was just confusion from being ill so long, but I suspected it was much more.

"Why didn't you give up?" I asked Phil.

"You," he said softly. "Because of you."

He smiled at my quizzical look and continued, "No, I'm not crazy. Everything seemed to change the night you stood in this very spot and held my hand. It was the night of the bad storm. You must have been caught in the rain because your shirtsleeve was soaking wet.

"Everyone who has touched me has done so with a purpose—to draw blood, change a dressing, and listen to my chest—and I couldn't help but notice how cold it felt. They were just doing a job, no different than my secretary taking messages at work. You came in here just to hold my hand—nothing else. The warmth of that touch felt like a hot shower had been turned on inside of me, and I felt changed. In those moments, there seemed to be more important things to think about than death, and I never seemed to get back to those dark thoughts again.

"I've always known what was important in life but just never got around to doing it, thinking that there would always be time. The past few days, I've realized just how short time can be, and I will never again let it pass unfulfilled."

Doctors are trained in the rational world, and logical thought hovers over our work to protect us from moments that don't seem to fit the scientific method. That a man could have such vivid recollections from when he lay unconscious was just one of those moments. It was easy to dismiss until with a start, I remembered that night. Indeed, it had been storming. I was soaking wet from the short walk across the doctors' parking lot.

With all of its technology, complexity, and traditions, it seems much too simplistic to consider touch in medicine. Physicians touch their patients constantly—to feel a pulse, palpate an abdomen, or percuss lung fields. It is a clinical touch. It is touch through which cure happens. My teachers have helped me discover another kind of touch—the hand grasp held longer than that required for greeting, a gentle hand placed on a shoulder, or a soft pat on the back. This is a healing touch, one that has helped make the improbable, probable.

# Simple Steps for Putting the Fifth Secret to Work

- Throughout the next day, take notice of how often you touch people, whether they are family, friends, or strangers.

- Observe your patterns of touching others as you do your work. Is touch an important part of your work? Does it make you uncomfortable? Select one word to describe the feelings you have when you must touch someone at work.

- Think about your best friend and the occasions during which you touch each other. How is the feeling different than with a stranger at work?

- Find a moment in your memories when someone's touch made you feel better—a congratulatory handshake, a hand of understanding placed on your back, or a feeling of closeness when they put an arm around your shoulders.

- A healing touch starts with *intention*, a desire to make someone feel better. A professional touch gets a job done.

- With every encounter discover the intention to make someone feel better with touch, if only for a moment, by lingering in your handshake a few seconds longer, resting your hand upon another's, or by offering a timely hug. It is magic that will change a professional touch into one of healing.

Whenever I climb, I am followed by a dog called Ego.
—Friedrich Nietzsche

The ego is not master in its own house.
—Sigmund Freud

*The Sixth Secret*

# Leave Your Ego
# at the Door

I was frustrated beyond belief. Mary Clements sat there looking at me as if nothing was wrong.

"What do you mean you didn't have surgery?" I asked incredulously. "Didn't you see Dr. Roscoe?"

"I did," she said simply.

"And," I pried, "what did he say?"

"He agreed with you," she said. "He said that I needed an operation and that I needed it right away."

"Well?" I asked, holding out my hands looking for more.

"He's not touching me," she said emphatically. "He might be a doctor, and he's certainly smarter than I am, but he's the most arrogant person I've ever met. He told me that the operation would be difficult because I was so fat and that he was very picky about the patients he selected. Complications could hurt his reputation, but as a favor to you, he was going to take the risk and take my case."

"You don't have to like the man, Mary," I argued, "but we need his skill. It's like hiring the best mechanic in town to work on your car."

"But I'm not a car," she said calmly. "Maybe I'm making a big mistake, but I have to believe that a doctor's skill is not nearly as important as what you find in their heart."

Her words were piercing and left me a little stunned and more than a little embarrassed. I had been so focused on getting her abdominal hernia repaired, on finding cure, that I had lost sight of healing.

Mary had been having abdominal pain for several months and only sought help when the severity of the pain became too great to hide from her family. The CT scan revealed a large abdominal hernia, and without surgery, she could develop a bowel obstruction at any moment. Unfortunately, few surgeons in the area accepted her state medical card, and those who did had waiting lists months long. I spent many hours on the telephone, making personal appeals on her behalf and was feeling rather proud of myself for getting her an appointment with such a fine surgeon as Dr. Roscoe. But I had forgotten an important secret of healing that I had first encountered many years earlier at the teaching hospital.

Not long after joining the faculty at the teaching hospital, I had been introduced to Gwen Morton during morning rounds. Much like Mary, the forty-five-year-old lady agreed to be brought to the emergency room only after months of discomfort. Four years earlier, Gwen had found a lump in her breast while showering one morning, and it had turned out to be breast cancer. The lump had been successfully removed, but one of the lymph nodes removed from under her arm during surgery had contained cancer cells.

Gwen's oncologist recommended chemotherapy, but she was terrified at the thought. Her best friend from college had had leukemia, and Gwen had sat with her for hours after the chemotherapy treatments, trying to offer meager comfort from the relentless nausea and vomiting. She had watched as the end of her friend's journey was consumed not by her disease, but by the treatment directed against the disease. Gwen's oncologist was very angry that she had questioned his judgment, and after many pitched battles about alternatives to chemotherapy, she just stopped going to the office.

While doing laundry one day, Gwen experienced sudden back pain while bending over for a clothes basket. Her husband had had problems with an old back injury, and the severity of her own discomfort made her wish that she had given him more sympathy throughout the years. Her family doctor diagnosed muscle strain, and she improved with muscle relaxants and anti-inflammatory medication. During the weeks that followed, however, her pain returned, its frequency and duration growing every week. Often, her legs felt heavy and weak, and at times she had to use her hands to help lift her leg when getting out of bed in the morning. When she couldn't get out of bed one morning, she surrendered to her family's demands to go to the hospital.

For a junior faculty member with his first team of medical students and residents, Gwen's admission seemed too good to be true. The description and progression of her pain, her history of breast cancer, and the findings on her physical examination provided a treasure trove of material from which to teach during rounds. Gwen was an *interesting case*—something that nobody wants to be in a teaching hospital.

Gwen's case was also an easy one to diagnose, regrettably so. Even the medical students figured it out. A CT scan of her spine confirmed everyone's suspicion. Two vertebrae in her thoracic spine had been eaten away by a mass that was now compressing her spinal cord. Most likely the breast cancer was back and had spread to the spine. It was a huge problem for Gwen. Radiation therapy would reduce the pain, but she was in danger of paralysis. We could treat, but cure seemed out of reach.

After rounds that first day, I sat outside Gwen's room in the intensive care unit, completing my paperwork. Two of my medical students sat nearby, polishing their write-ups to perfection. I was pleased to see the arrival of her oncologist with the consult team—a familiar face was just what she needed. But I was wrong.

"Gwen, what have you done?" exclaimed her oncologist in a voice that carried throughout the ICU. "I warned you that this would happen. I'm never wrong about cancer, but you just wouldn't listen, would you? Such a waste. All of this could have been prevented. Look what you have done to your family."

Loud sobs were the only reply to the angry doctor's tirade. The ICU grew uncommonly quiet—even the incessant noise from the bedside monitors seemed to retreat into the silence. Nurses exchanged knowing looks—they had seen such tantrums before. My medical students had not, at least not from the likes of an attending physician, and their faces turned as white as their crisp new lab coats.

As the oncologist strode from Gwen's room with a team of residents trailing behind, I struggled to hide the surprise that I felt with a senior colleague. He had always been a pompous figure, certainly not a rarity in academic medicine. The center of attention suited him, frequently rising to ask questions or offer comments during grand rounds and conferences, comments that seldom seemed to add substance to the discussion at hand. He was quick to note that his patients' survival rates far exceeded the national averages for cancer patients, and I couldn't help but wonder if this was the source of his anger with Gwen. Her tumor recurrence might reflect badly on him.

The halls and conference rooms of the teaching hospital can breed powerful egos. They are so commonplace that you tend not to notice after a while. It had never occurred to me that ego would be brought to the bedside or taken into the examination room. But as I look back on that day, I realize that ego is a physician's frequent companion, albeit typically subtle and hidden in the genuine desire to cure.

Is it the understanding of the myriad complications from hypertension that frustrates a doctor when their patient does not take the medications that they prescribed? Could it be a concern for delayed treatment that stings a physician when a long-followed patient asks for a second opinion? Might it be an apprehension toward untested therapies that alarms a doctor when a patient wants to consider a holistic approach? Is it respect for a therapeutic relationship that startles a physician when addressed by their first name? Or could it be ego?

Frustration, alarm, feeling stung, and being startled—along with the souls who bring such emotion into my life—are among my greatest teachers. They come with the gentle reminder that it is not about me—it is, and always will be, about my patients. When ego walks with us, sometimes we find our greatest cures. It is only when we leave our ego at the door, however, that we find our greatest potential to heal.

# *Simple Steps for Putting the Sixth Secret to Work*

- Start every encounter with a silent acknowledgment—this has nothing to do with me, it's all about the person whom I am here to help.
- Be alert for feelings of frustration, anger, and irritation. They are reminders that our ego is always nearby.
- There is a feeling of calm when an interaction takes place free of ego. When that calm disappears, look for ways that your ego has taken over.
- A brief pause, a deep breath, and a silent affirmation of *how may I help* will push the ego aside and make healing possible.

There are only two ways to live your life. One is as though nothing is a miracle. The other is as though everything is a miracle.

—Albert Einstein

No man can reveal to you nothing but that which already lies half-asleep in the dawning of your knowledge.

—Kahlil Gibran

Miracles are not contrary to nature, but only contrary to what we know about nature.

—St. Augustine

*The Seventh Secret*

# Dare to Believe
# in Miracles

IT was like watching a parent try to reason with a five-year-old boy who knew nothing about the logic of the adult world and could only ask, "Why?" when faced with the seeming absurdity of conventional wisdom.

"Didn't Mrs. Winston get the chest CT?" Dr. Taylor asked the medical resident in disbelief. "This is horrible!"

"Why?" the young doctor asked.

"Because we dropped the ball," his faculty supervisor replied.

"How did we do that?" the resident asked.

"By not getting the scan," the senior doctor replied, the loudness of his voice growing with obvious frustration.

"Why?" asked the resident again.

"Because," the older doctor nearly shouted, "I said to get one."

It was the parental trump card designed to stifle debate, and just as it was failing around breakfast tables all across the country, it did little to end this debate on terms favorable to the teaching physician. Madge Winston had returned to the medicine clinic at the teaching hospital for a follow-up appointment. Two months earlier she had sought out her clinic doctor for a cough that wouldn't go away. She was a smoker, and her family was worried because she was losing weight. The chest X-ray obtained that day hung from the light box in the clinic's conference room. Medical students and residents crowded around to see the large mass in the lower lobe of her left lung.

"You mean you sent her for a surgery consultation without a CT scan?" Dr. Taylor asked.

"Why would I send her to surgery?" Madge's young doctor asked.

"Because that's how we treat lung cancer, Doctor," the exasperated physician replied. "We certainly don't use antibiotics. What in the world did you do for her?"

"I put her on antibiotics," came the meek reply.

"You are kidding, aren't you?" the stunned-looking faculty doctor asked in disbelief.

"No, sir," answered the resident. "I spent more than an hour with her talking about it. She asked me if it could be an infection, and I told her that there was no way to be certain from a chest X-ray but that we all thought it was a tumor. She told me that she knew her body better than we did, and she was certain that we were mistaken. She asked me to treat her for pneumonia, and so I did."

The conference room grew hushed, an improbable event in a clinic filled with so many resident physicians and their senior mentors. I had known Stan Taylor for many years. He taught with an abrasive and confrontational style, and it was the first time that I could remember having seen him at a loss for words. He ran his hands through his thinning hair and looked about the room nervously, as if looking for help. His face, typically expressionless, now looked worried.

"Son," he said softly, almost compassionately, "this was a mistake, and a bad one. We're talking about lung cancer here. These two months may have cost this lady the chance for cure.

"Of course she wanted to believe this was pneumonia, but miracles just don't happen in medicine. You are her doctor. It was your job to convince her of that. Antibiotics don't cure lung cancer, and by giving them to her, you gave her a false sense of hope.

"We have to move fast now. Hopefully, it's not too late. Let's get another chest X-ray today and then schedule a CT."

"But Dr. Taylor," the resident said cautiously, "she doesn't have lung cancer. I already got another chest film this morning."

With that, the junior medical resident flipped another film onto the light box next to the image from two months earlier. Sure enough, the lung fields were clear and pristine. What had appeared to be a large mass earlier had vanished entirely.

The shocked look on the senior doctor's face lasted only a moment.

Shaking his head he said, "No, there has obviously been

a mistake. Either this film was done on the wrong patient, or the first one was."

"No, sir," defended the resident. "I just knew the X-ray would be better, but I wasn't expecting it to be clear, so I checked to make sure. Look here," he said pointing to the shadow made by the left clavicle. "Mrs. Winston fractured her shoulder five years ago. You can see it on both films."

Putting on a pair of well-used reading glasses, Dr. Taylor studied each image intently, moving back and forth to compare them. Dropping his glasses to the conference table, he dropped into a chair with a loud sigh.

"Sure enough," he said, "it's gone. But it still looks like lung cancer to me. Why were you so sure that it was just pneumonia?"

"Well, I wasn't," the resident replied. "I thought it was lung cancer, too, and still do."

Shaking his head in confusion, the mentor asked, "Then why did you give her antibiotics?"

"Because she wanted them," the young doctor said, "and although it seemed unlikely to be infection, it was still a possibility. You always tell us that patients have the right to make their own decisions, even bad ones. Maybe it was her taking control of her illness that got her better, and the antibiotics didn't have a thing to do with it."

With a furrowed brow the elder doctor looked at his

young colleague through narrowed eyes and asked, "Are you suggesting that the antibiotics were a placebo?"

The resident was silent for many moments before replying, "Not if the mass was pneumonia after all. But if it was indeed lung cancer, then I'm not sure what it was. But Dr. Taylor, you mentioned that miracles don't occur in medicine. Isn't the placebo effect a miracle?"

It was a profound question for a physician to contemplate, particularly one so young. Perhaps, however, it was that very youth that made it possible to ponder the possibility of miracles. Extraordinary events that occur without explanation are commonplace in medicine, often uncomfortably so to its practitioners. The untrained eye would call them miracles. The scientific eye, however, struggles to find other possibilities. So desperate are some to discount the possibility of miracles, and the acknowledgment that healing can occur without the physician, that refuge is sought in the placebo effect.

We are taught in medical school that it is not unusual for one third of patients with a given medical condition to improve after receiving a placebo. Thirty percent of a medication's effects might not have anything to do with its active ingredients. Strangely missing from those lessons, however, was the wonder and the invitation to contemplate something greater than ourselves. Madge Winston's doctor was right. The placebo effect was a miracle, one of countless miracles that can be found by those who look for them.

Like most physicians, I have had patients get better when our science predicted otherwise. I have encountered success for which I had not the skill to achieve. I have discovered the correct answer despite not having the knowledge. I have found the right words when I lacked the wisdom for what to say. At one point on my journey, I confused this with the definition of a physician. My teachers, however, have helped me recognize the miracle.

When you buy a new car, you tend to see the same make and model wherever you go. Such is the case with miracles. Once you embrace their possibility in your personal and professional life, you encounter them everywhere. It is through the willingness to accept the wondrous and unexpected as something greater than ourselves that we allow others to find miracles, and healing, in their lives.

# Simple Steps for Putting the Seventh Secret to Work

- Carry an index card in your pocket. Every time you encounter an experience that defies explanation— an accomplishment that seems beyond your ability, a sudden understanding where only confusion had been before, an automobile that narrowly avoids disaster, or finding oneself in just the right place at just the right time—write it down. Could there be miracles in such experiences?

- Pause for a moment to reflect on those everyday events that we take for granted but can not explain— the thought that moves a hand, a desire to have or to become, feeling love, or a butterfly migrating across a continent. Could there be miracles in such events?

- In every encounter, be open to the possibility that you will discover a miracle.

Knowledge is knowing that we cannot know.

—Ralph Waldo Emerson

When you know a thing, to hold that you know it; and when you do not know a thing, to allow that you do not know it—this is knowledge.

—Confucius

*The Eighth Secret*

# Embrace the
# Unknown

I cringed when I walked into the examination room and saw my new patient waiting for me. On his lap he clutched a thick folder stuffed with papers. A large envelope overflowing with X-ray films leaned against his chair. A notepad sat next to him on the desk. They were relics from a journey that he had traveled through medicine, one that he most likely found lacking. He needed something, and that search had led to my office. Sometimes it was a search for medication that others had denied him. Sometimes it was a search for understanding that had been lost through the rituals and language of modern medicine. Sometimes it was a search for a listening ear. Whatever this man was looking for, it would consume much more time than my busy schedule offered.

He said nothing as I sat in my chair across from him. His hand trembled a little as he handed me the folder. Its contents were meticulously organized; there were letters from physicians and consultants, summaries of hospital admissions, and pages upon pages of laboratory and test results. The top several sheets chronicled his journey and touched my heart.

Norman Brinker was my age although he looked a good bit older. A few weeks earlier, he had started to have abdominal pain. The pain was more of a nuisance than anything else, and it had shared in his daily routine for many days, perhaps gradually increasing in intensity. Work had been unusually stressful of late, and Norman was fairly certain that the upper abdominal pain was the sign of an ulcer. The antacids he bought at the drugstore helped, but when yellow eyes peered back at him from the bathroom mirror one morning, he realized that something else had been brewing.

Dr. Stephens, his family doctor, called it jaundice and reassured Norman that the discomfort he had been feeling was actually good news because painless jaundice was typically associated with bad things. Blood tests and a CT scan of the abdomen were ordered to investigate the suspected hepatitis or gallstone that had obstructed a duct. Several lines from the chronology leapt from the page:

December 1, 6:15 PM, Dr. Stephens called during dinner.

"I was wrong, it is bad. It's a tumor and is most likely cancer. My office will call you with the name of a surgeon and cancer specialist in the morning."

Indeed, it was cancer. The biopsy demonstrated a particularly aggressive pancreatic cancer. Laboratory studies already indicated ailing liver and kidney function. Imaging revealed that the tumor had already spread to surrounding structures. I didn't see that many CT scans, but even I could see the tumor on the film that I held up to the light. It was huge.

Returning the film to its envelope and closing his folder, I looked into his eyes. They still had a hint of yellow to them. We still hadn't spoken, but those eyes told of a gentle soul who was haunted by unaccustomed fear and an overwhelming need to know.

"What can I do for you, Mr. Brinker?" I asked softly.

"My oncologist tells me that I will live for six months with chemotherapy," he replied, "and two months without. Another oncologist only gives me a few weeks. If I have an operation, the surgeon says that I will live nine months, perhaps a year. I need to know, how long do I have? When am I going to die?"

"I don't know," I said to him.

They were among my most powerful words in medicine and as was often the case, saying them took me back to an earlier time when a special teacher had taught me something extraordinary about healing.

Sandra Quail had sat in my office, much like Norman did now, with a thick folder of records and a long list of questions. I had been the sixth doctor from whom she had sought answers as to why she did not feel well; the records from the previous five were meticulously preserved in the folder that had become an extension of her life. It had been a bad sign—one predictive of long, painful visits with a difficult patient that was unlikely to end well.

Sandra's search for answers had started almost two years before although some notations in her records made mention that she had no recollection of ever feeling well. She hurt all over: abdomen, chest, joints, and muscles. At times she had even thought that her hair hurt. The abdominal pain was the worst. Some days it came with diarrhea, while other days she suffered from constipation.

Fatigue was a constant companion of Sandra, which made it impossible for her to work or enjoy life. She could sleep most anytime of the day, except at night when she would lay awake. The pain was always worse at night. Hardly a week passed when headaches, dizziness, shortness of breath, or heart palpitations took her to the emergency room, and often she was there two or three times a week. She worried about hair loss and the twenty-five pounds of weight that had mysteriously disappeared. All she wanted was to feel good.

Fibromyalgia, chronic fatigue syndrome, irritable bowel syndrome, and chronic pain syndrome were among Sandra's litany of diagnoses. More than one of her physicians felt that she was depressed. They had tried countless medications, each had been started with high expectations of success only to be withdrawn in frustration days later because of nausea, anxiety, or her complaint, "Doc, it made me feel funny."

Like those described by my predecessors, my examination of Sandra revealed nothing out of the ordinary for a healthy thirty-five-year-old lady, except for her sadness. Sadness hovered over her like an overcast sky. I felt sad being around her. Of the scores of test results contained in her folder, I could not find one abnormality. Resisting the impulse to order more tests and hasten her exit with yet another prescription, we elected to watch and wait for a while. Every several weeks, Sandra came to my office, and I went about the ritual of an examination that never changed. She described her feelings of illness, often referring to the detailed notes she had kept.

Toward of the end of Sandra's third visit, she looked me in the eye and asked, "So, Doctor, what is wrong with me?"

"I do not know," I said, letting the words penetrate a full minute before continuing. "I can tell you what's not causing your problems, and sometimes, that's the best we can do in medicine. But I can't tell you why you feel bad. What I can do is see you on a regular basis and be alert for anything that we may need to act upon."

Sandra didn't keep her follow-up appointment, and after several months, I assumed that she had moved on to doctor number seven. Almost a year later, her name reappeared on my schedule. I almost didn't recognize her when I walked into the exam room. She had gained weight, was well dressed, and had changed her hairstyle. She was smiling and to my shock, looked happy.

"Wow," I said in surprise, "You look great. When did this happen?"

She smiled broadly and said, "It started the minute I left this office the last time. What you said hit me like a bolt of lightning."

"What did I say?" I asked.

If I was going to get credit for doing something that helped this most difficult of patients, then I wanted to know what it was.

"You said you didn't know," she said. "I have never heard a doctor say that before. All of my other doctors didn't have a clue, but they wouldn't say so. They all thought it was all in my head. Maybe it was, and maybe you thought so, too, but you didn't say it. I left here feeling that perhaps I wasn't imagining it all. You were willing to keep an open mind, and I knew that if I needed you, I could come back. But you know, I discovered that I didn't need you. I came back today to say thank you. Thank you for not knowing."

Norman looked a bit startled at my words, and I placed a reassuring hand upon his.

"You're not the first to ask that question, and my answer is always the same. I don't know. I do not have the knowledge, or the wisdom, to answer your question.

"But is it really important? I could guess and come up

with a date. But then, you would spend the rest of your life looking toward that date rather than living in the present moment. Despite the cancer, you could get struck by a truck and die tomorrow. So maybe it's more important to concentrate on today."

Norman Brinker did just that. Not knowing what tomorrow would bring made each day special and important. He found time to read the classics and listen to country music. He rediscovered painting and was fulfilled in the realization that their beauty and message would live on for him. He discovered family and shared something with a small boy that only a grandfather could make special. He was touched by beauty daily and marveled at how it had eluded him before. His journey lasted another eighteen months—a lifetime—and while he did not find cure, he was healed through not knowing.

# Simple Steps for Putting the Eighth Secret to Work

- In your moments of silence, think of something that you know nothing about—the forest floor, a singing songbird, distant nebulae, or perhaps, the energy we perceive as light. How does that thought make you feel?

- Picture children at play exploring sand dunes along the ocean's shore. Feel the excitement of not knowing what could be found over the distant rise.

- Treasure every question asked to which you know the answer. It is an opportunity to share knowledge.

- Treasure, even more, the question to which you do not know the answer. It offers the chance to say, "I do not know," and to share something of the unknown with another. It is in that unknown that we can find healing.

Natural forces within us are the true healers of disease.

—Hippocrates

Be fully in the moment, open yourself to the powerful energies dancing around you.

—Ernest Hemingway

The only ones among you who will be really happy are those who will have sought and found how to serve.

—Albert Schweitzer

*The Ninth Secret*

# It's All
# About Energy

I hated starting the day late. It always seemed to bring hours of frustration and angst to my life. It was in the midst of such chaos one morning that my teachers paid me a visit.

Mrs. Quint sat waiting anxiously when I walked into the examination room fifteen minutes late. The eighty-four-year-old widow clutched a list in her hands, a list that she had spent most of the night adding to. Insomnia was one of the things that she wanted to talk about. She had arthritis and experienced pain almost every waking moment. Not being able to sleep just added to those waking moments. As she looked at the length of her list, she realized that her health was worse than she had thought. Once she started listing her problems, they just seemed to go on forever.

Peter Straw waited his turn in the next room. He was having trouble sleeping, too. Three times that week, he woke to sudden awareness that something was wrong—his heart beat too loudly, his breathing was too shallow, and his skin was too sensitive. He knew that something was seriously wrong.

Jackie Boyles needed to be seen urgently. She had abdominal pain. It had started several years earlier—shortly after her grandfather had died from colon cancer—and had never gone away, even for a moment. The doctor who did the colonoscopy one month earlier had obviously missed something, as did the doctor that had done one six months before that.

Shortness of breath brought Ben Miller to the office. It was his third visit that month. The pulmonologist and cardiologist to whom I had sent him couldn't explain his symptoms any better than I could. His shortness of breath strangely appeared every morning shortly after breakfast. Stranger still, he realized that he never seemed to have trouble on Sundays. Ben was a human resources director who was responsible for carrying out the recent job reductions ordered by the large company he worked for.

I longed for a sore throat, a blood pressure check, or even a rash, anything that was quick, but it was not too be. Every patient consumed more time than the one who came before them, each with problems capable of sucking life from those who ventured too close, problems that seemed to defy solution. While still early in my morning, it was clear that I had ventured too close. I felt exhausted and more than a little reluctant to see my next patient.

To my surprise, the next examination room was empty and so was the next. The waiting room was empty as well.

"Where is Mrs. White?" I asked my nurse.

Erin just smiled, took hold of my arm, and led me down the hall to my office.

"Where is everyone?" I asked again.

The lights in my office were dimmed and soft music was playing from the stereo. On my desk sat a steaming cup of coffee and my favorite danish, obviously from the neighborhood bakery just down the street.

"I rescheduled your next four patients," Erin said softly.

"Why?" I asked.

"You didn't eat today, did you?" Erin asked in her typical way of answering a question with another question.

"No," I said. "I had a number of calls during the night and wound up sleeping late. The dogs ran through mud and tracked up the kitchen, the drain in the shower backed up, and the smoke detector decided to go off for no apparent reason. Then, I couldn't find my keys. Why did you reschedule the patients?"

"Because you need to eat," she said emphatically, "and then you need a little quiet time before we can change the direction of this day. It's either this, or I'm going to have to take your belt and shoelaces away from you."

I smiled at her attempt at humor and her caring. She really knew me well; it was uncanny. We had been together a long time, since I completed residency and started my practice. I thought I knew a lot about medicine in those days, and perhaps I did, but I knew little about healing. Erin taught me everything that she knew.

Erin had an incredible gift with people. You felt better just being around her. I always knew when Erin had checked in one of my patients—invariably they were smiling and no matter how ill they might have been, they always commented that they were suddenly feeling a little better. Often, I couldn't be sure if my patients were coming to see me or Erin. The elderly loved her, and she loved them. She sat with them, held their hands, and listened to their stories. There was an energy to Erin, a powerful energy that reached out from her soul and touched all in its path, whether they wanted to be touched or not.

I was stunned one morning to arrive at work and find Erin sitting with Herb Grouse. He was certainly among those who didn't want to be touched by anyone's energy. A widower long since retired, he was perhaps the angriest and most bitter man I had ever encountered. His life was one of scarcity and loneliness, and his demeanor did nothing to foster change. Yet there he sat with Erin, a subtle but unmistakable smile on his face. She had learned that in his younger days he had collected seashells, and so on one of his office visits, she gave him a cigar box filled with brightly colored shells that had been collecting dust in her attic. Each week and sometimes more often than that, he stopped by the office to show Erin a special shell, one connected to a soul who had been deeply hidden for many years. In that soul a younger man's dreams had waited patiently until just the right person and just the right energy had brought them to life. I might have treated his blood pressure, but it was Erin who had brought him healing.

"We forget just how powerful our thoughts are," Erin seemed to think out loud as I drank my coffee and relaxed that morning. "It just sneaks up on us. Something bad happens—we oversleep—and it changes the way we feel. The worse we feel, the more bad things we seem to attract. The more bad things we attract, the worse we feel. Pretty soon, the entire day is in a shambles. My mother always says, 'What you think about happens.'"

Erin was a master at using energy to heal. How I wish I had paid closer attention in physics class during high school and college. Albert Einstein taught us that "everything is energy" and that "nothing happens until something moves." It is the speed of those moving particles and the frequency of the energy that impacts how we feel.

Thought is nothing more than energy. Indeed, what we think about happens. As Mrs. Quint thought about her problems, her problems multiplied. The more Jackie Boyles worried about colon cancer, the worse her abdominal pain got. The closer Ben Miller got to a difficult job, the more difficult it was for him to breathe. Imagined symptoms? Of course not, but symptoms influenced nonetheless by the energy of thought.

What would be embraced by the quantum physicist

can be difficult to accept for patients and physicians whose science is rooted in that which we can see, touch, and measure. The inability to measure thought, however, does not make it less real. We do not question that the thought of food can produce saliva and an increase in gastric secretions; that a frightening image can elicit increased blood pressure, heart rate, and serum adrenaline levels; or that a romantic contemplation can change our bodies in profound ways.

Worry, anxiety, guilt, and shame are among thoughts with the lowest of energy and nurture pain, fatigue, and illness. Raise the energy of our thoughts with feelings of gratitude, love, and generosity, and our problems start to melt away. In an instant, we can change our thoughts and change how we feel.

Erin had a knack at getting people to change their thoughts. It wasn't her knowledge of quantum mechanics or her understanding of the cellular effects of energy; she just knew how to make people feel better. Within minutes she could have the forlorn laughing at a joke, reveling in the pride of a child, or reliving a beautiful sunset, and in those moments of changed thoughts, they found a glimpse of peace and a moment of healing upon which to build.

Erin instinctively knew that how she felt influenced how others felt. Like that special person who is the hit of the party and makes everyone smile or the unfortunate soul at work whom everyone tries to avoid, our level of energy can change that of others. Even when having a difficult day, I never saw Erin without a smile in front of a patient. Before facing particularly challenging prospects, Erin had a habit of taking several deep breaths and standing quietly for a minute or two with a broad smile on her face. When asked about this behavior, she again shared the wisdom from her mother, "You can't give what you don't have." She had plenty to give.

Healers intuitively know the need to maintain high levels of energy in their lives and how to go about achieving it: they choose friends and associates with care, they appreciate and seek out beauty, they look for the best in others, they find comfort in quiet, and they give of themselves.

It is the act of giving that perhaps most nourishes healing energy. I discovered it quite unexpectedly in a free medical clinic in the hills of Appalachia. Through two decades and thousands of patients, I have received much more than I have given. It doesn't take much money or a lot of time to experience the power of giving, however. It can be found in a door held open for a stranger, a telephone answered in a pleasant voice, or a generous tip at a restaurant. It is through the service of others, no matter what our work may be, that we can be healers.

# Simple Steps for Putting the Ninth Secret to Work

- *You can't give what you don't have.* Place index cards with these words where you will see them throughout the day and be reminded that it is difficult to care for others if we do not first take care of ourselves.

- Spend a few moments every day making a conscious effort to increase your energy to a higher, faster level. Pause in the awareness and appreciation of a sunrise, a garden patch, or the soliloquy of a song bird. Linger a bit longer in the presence of a special friend or the perfect stranger, who somehow makes you feel good. Give something of yourself without any expectation of return—complimenting a coworker, helping the elderly lady next door move her trash to the curb, or paying for that stranger's coffee standing in line behind you. It energizes your ability to help others heal.

- Be alert for thoughts that lower your energy—anger, jealousy, and judgment of others. Awareness is the first step to changing those thoughts.

- When feeling down or out-of-sorts, picture a luscious red rose with dew clinging to delicate petals, a favorite painting hanging in a museum, or a flotilla of goslings ushered by proud parents across the glass surface of an emerald pond—you have just changed your thoughts.

- Approach every encounter with the thought, "How can I help?"

- A smile is a characteristic of healing energy. Wear one always. When it seems to be difficult, *fake it 'til you make it.*

The only real valuable thing is intuition.

—Albert Einstein

No ray of sunlight is ever lost, but the green that it wakes needs time to sprout, and it is not always granted to the sower to see the harvest. All work that is worth anything is done in faith.

—Albert Schweitzer

*The Tenth Secret*

# Trust Your Intuition

**F**RIDAYS were special, not because it represented the end of the workweek—a simple pleasure that a medical career had rendered extinct—but because it meant having clinic in the country. It was a place where practicing medicine seemed most pure, where the barriers of technology, administrators, and the expectations of others who always seemed to get in the way during the week dared not intrude. It was a place where teaching and learning did not come from conferences, journal articles, or the considered opinions advanced on morning rounds but from simple and magical lives. There was no better place to learn about healing. I remember the lessons particularly well from one spring afternoon.

It was the first warm day of the year, one long awaited after an unusually cold and snowy winter. The drive from the city was like a journey into sanctuary, one so peaceful that you hated to see it end. Joe Thompson rode out with me. Nearing the end of his first-year of residency training, he had lost much of the fear that had haunted his first months as a doctor. It was a time for mastering skills and gaining confidence in the tools of his trade. It was a favorite time for me to spend with the residents—they were eager to learn and not yet set in the ways of tradition.

It was quickly apparent that Joe had learned his lessons well and was developing into a fine physician. Without thick files of medical history and diagnostic studies to review, he started, perhaps for the first time, to listen to the stories of his patients. Those stories thrilled him. He learned about chopping and splitting wood, milking cows, and where the largest and tastiest mushrooms could be found. He began to realize that the story was just as important as the examination.

Jake Crawford was having trouble with indigestion. It only bothered him at night after going to bed. It was a burning a pain in the pit of his stomach that made it difficult to sleep. He started taking soda water before going to bed, but it didn't help very much. Joe did a thorough examination, probably more thorough than I would have done and found nothing out of the ordinary.

"I think it's reflux disease," Joe reported to me confidently. "Let's put him on an H2 blocker. He should be better in a few days."

He grinned with the satisfaction of a schoolboy when I agreed with his diagnosis and treatment. But it wasn't pride that elated him so much. It was the contentment of helping someone who just minutes earlier had been a stranger and now seemed strangely like a friend.

Barely an hour passed before Joe voiced his dismay with the similarities between two of his patients.

"What is it with the country?" he asked. "I've just seen my second reflux patient. They could be twins."

James Carson had been having trouble with indigestion. It only bothered him at night after going to bed. It was a burning pain in the pit of his stomach, and it had been waking him an hour or two before dawn the past several days. He started taking soda water before going to bed, but it didn't help very much. His examination, like Jake's before him, had been entirely normal.

"Let's put him on an H2 blocker, too." Joe suggested.

"It does sound like reflux," I said after spending a few minutes with James, "and I think the H2 blocker is fine, but let's schedule him for a treadmill stress test, too. See if we can get it done first thing on Monday."

If he was perplexed by my suggestion, Joe didn't voice it as he set about making arrangements for his patient to travel to the teaching hospital early Monday morning for a stress test. On the drive home that evening, Joe seemed unusually pensive, and I couldn't decide if he was troubled by something or simply tired. It had been a long day.

It was late the following Monday when a soft knocking at my office door distracted me from some paperwork. It was Joe, and he seemed upset.

"How did you know that Mr. Carson didn't have reflux in the clinic last Friday?" he asked softly.

"Well, I didn't," I responded quizzically. "I thought he

could have had reflux, and that's why we treated him. Why? What's wrong?"

"I haven't been able to stop thinking about him all weekend," Joe replied, clearly frustrated. "I don't know what I missed. The stress test idea just seemed to come from nowhere. I was so certain that you were wrong that I met Mr. Carson this morning for his exercise test."

"And," I urged him on, "what happened?"

Joe looked at me in disbelief for several moments before answering, "He coded on the treadmill this morning. They took him to the cath lab and found an occlusion of the right coronary artery and extensive three-vessel disease. He is in the OR right now for emergency bypass surgery. I need to know, sir, just how did you know?"

"I didn't know, Joe," I tried to reassure him. "You didn't miss anything, and you didn't do anything wrong. It would have been proper to have sent Mr. Carson home just with medication, like you did for Mr. Crawford."

"And he might be dead now if I had," observed Joe sadly. "If he had been any other place than here when he arrested, he never would have survived. But why do a stress test for reflux?"

"I'm not sure I can give you a good explanation," I told him, "at least, not one that you will find in the medical literature. Something didn't add up with Mr. Carson. He never complains and never goes to see the doctor, but there he was in clinic with a problem that seemed just too minor for him to be complaining about. We all have an inner voice that speaks to us, and I've found that the more I listen to it, the better a doctor I am."

"Wow," Joe seemed to think out loud, "all of these years learning about the differential diagnosis when all you really need is intuition."

It seemed like only yesterday that I too struggled with differential diagnosis, the practice of listing all of the possible causes of a constellation of symptoms. It was a tool handed down throughout the ages, one that sharpened the mind and focused the pursuit of cure. Often, however, I found it lacking.

"Joe," I said, "intuition doesn't replace anything that we do in medicine. It adds to it and makes it more powerful. Take Mr. Carson, for example. It's not uncommon for cardiac symptoms to occur in the early-morning hours, nor is it unusual for the very lesion that was found on his cardiac cath to cause only symptoms of indigestion or nausea. Heart disease was always on the list of possibilities. Intuition simply helped us put it on the top of the list.

"Intuition can help us better use what we know or perhaps more importantly, to tell us when we don't know enough. Many a night I have sat up reading because of that nagging voice telling me that I was missing something. More than once it led me to the right answer, and when it didn't, I always seemed to learn something that would help someone else later on."

Like Joe, I had been a young resident when I had first faced the possibility that intuition might have a place in medicine. My teacher was Agnes Hahn, a name and face who still walks with me, unblemished by the passage of time. I had been taking care of Agnes the better part of a week when she asked me to sit and talk with her one evening. She had a mass in her hung that we didn't know what it was. It was a time before technology took medical imaging to wondrous heights, before MRI and PET scanners, and before interventional radiology. The opinions of experts were our best weapons, but the experts could not agree.

Agnes was the topic of daily rounds, special conferences, and heated debates. One group of specialists favored infection as the likely cause of her shortness of breath and the strange shadows on her chest X-ray and advocated weeks of antibiotics with follow-up X-rays. Another group of specialists were equally adamant that a tumor was the answer, and if surgical removal was delayed, even for a few weeks, the potential for cure could be lost. Complicating the picture was a bleeding disorder that was discovered when Agnes had an emergency appendectomy many years earlier. Lung surgery would not only be exceedingly difficult, but could be more dangerous than anything that would be found in the operating room.

"What do you feel, Doctor?" she asked me. "Is it infection or tumor?"

"That's probably a better question for the experts," I said uncomfortably.

"Have you been listening to them?" she asked incredulously. "They can't agree among themselves and don't seem the least bit concerned that I'm aware of it. It's all about them and who's right. You seem to be concerned about me. I want to know what you feel."

"I don't know the answer," I started to explain before she interrupted me.

"No, honey," she said, "Not what you *know* but what you *feel*. What does that inner voice tell you about me?"

"Mrs. Hahn, isn't it more important what that voice is telling you?" I asked.

"But you know more about medicine than I do, about what's reasonable and what's not," she countered. "What your intuition tells you is very valuable to me."

She waited patiently as I shifted uncomfortably from one foot to the other, searching for the right words.

"I'm concerned that this is tumor," I said softly, "and I worry about you taking too long to find out. Life is short."

Agnes left the hospital the following morning to spend time at home and reflect on her options. I didn't see her again until two years later when she sat in my examination room in the medical clinic of the teaching hospital. She had sought me out, and I was deeply touched.

She had opted for surgery. Indeed, a tumor had cast the shadows on her chest X-ray. It was lung cancer. Surgery went well, as had the years that followed. Each follow-up examination revealed that she was cancer free.

"I just wanted to thank you for spending time with me that night in the hospital," she told me. "I was so frightened and confused. You shared something precious with me, and it changed my life."

"I'm sure you would have decided on surgery regardless of me," I insisted.

"Perhaps," she said, "but the surgery was irrelevant. My father was a Baptist minister, but I spent most of my life oblivious to the wisdom that he shared with so many. I was an angry and rebellious young lady and couldn't wait to leave home the moment I was old enough. And I never looked back. I couldn't see that I had turned my back on my most important possession, my family. I didn't even attend my father's funeral.

"I thought a lot about my father when I was in the hospital. He had always spoken about listening to the inner voice when facing a difficult situation. I was never convinced that I could hear one, but all of a sudden, it became real important to try. That was why I asked you what you heard. When you told me that life was short, everything seemed so clear to me. I picked up the phone and called my sister. We hadn't spoken in more than ten years, but she showed up at the hospital that very night.

"My sister was the one who convinced me to have surgery, but it didn't really matter. What did matter was that I had my sister back in my life. Life is short, and I could have spent the rest of mine alone. I will never again question that voice that speaks to us when we listen for it. I just wanted to thank you for sharing yours with me."

Whether we call it intuition, an inner voice, or an awareness of universal wisdom that is always with us, it has become a valuable tool in my practice of medicine. Through it, there is more than cure—I have witnessed the wonders of healing.

# Simple Steps for Putting the Tenth Secret to Work

- Awareness of intuition is the first step in tapping its power. Throughout the day, take notice of the times when intuition speaks to you—the correct answer on a test, a fortuitous change in plans, the awareness of a friend or family member in need, or simply knowing that something will make you happy.

- The more you listen, the more you will hear. Practice listening for that inner voice in your moments of silence, and soon, you will discover it speaks to you often.

- Intuition is most clear when free from the influence of the ego. It is a powerful force when in the service of others. Making your encounters with others more about them, and less about you, will energize intuition.

- When faced with a making a decision, consider the possibility that the right answer is already present within you.

Most of us who turn to any subject we love remember some morning or evening hour when we got on a high stool to reach down an untried volume, or sat with parted lips listening to a new talker, or for very lack of books began to listen to the voices within, as the first traceable beginning of our love.

—George Eliot

Strange is our situation here on earth. Each of us comes for a short visit, not knowing why, yet sometimes seeming to divine a purpose.

—Albert Einstein

*The Eleventh Secret*

# Treat Each Encounter as if It Were Your Last

I studied the number that appeared on my pager but didn't recognize it. Strange numbers always frustrated me because I couldn't judge if it might be important. It was a moot point as I was too busy to answer it anyway, but it was hard to suppress the impulse cultured over the previous three years. By the time I had placed the last suture that secured the small catheter that I had inserted into my patient's artery, the number had appeared two more times on the pager's display.

I was in my final week of my final rotation of residency. If I had envisioned a quiet finale to the three years of training, I was sadly mistaken. I finished my residency in the intensive care unit, perhaps the most demanding of places for physicians in training. As busy as I was though, I still had time to help younger colleagues struggling with procedures. I smiled at the intern who had been hovering over my shoulder. His eyes reflected relief—that I had finally placed the arterial line—and frustration—that it had only taken me a few minutes to accomplish what he had struggled to do unsuccessfully at for more than an hour.

It didn't seem that long ago that I too had struggled at performing procedures, so much so that I once questioned whether I would ever learn the skills needed to become a good physician. I could only smile as I placed a dressing over the arterial line that pierced the flesh of the elderly man's wrist—it was probably the easiest arterial line I had ever placed. It's the way I had wanted it. There is not much call for such invasive procedures in the practice of internal medicine, and I knew that it was probably the last arterial line I would ever insert. I wanted it to be perfect and to reflect my best. It was, and it did.

Through countless sleepless nights, anxious vigils at bedsides of incredibly ill patients, and demanding, and finding the impossible from within, residency had transformed me into a highly skilled and confident physician. But as the hours of my residency waned, so did that confidence. In a few days, the skills that I had struggled to master, that had consumed much of my energy and thought these past three years of my life would become irrelevant. I knew how to shock a quiet heart back into life, to draw fluid from collapsed lungs and distended abdomens, to cure devastating disease, or to frustrate death when I could not, but I didn't know how to heal. It was a realization that shocked and haunted me.

Indeed it was a strange phone number, one that I had never been paged to before. It was from the medical arts building that stood next to the teaching hospital and housed the private practices of the medical school faculty. The practice receptionist told me that Dr. Wilder wanted to see me immediately.

"I'm in the ICU. Can you tell me what it's about?" I asked her.

"I believe he wants you to see a patient," she said.

"He knows that I am still in residency, doesn't he?" I asked, convinced that she had called the wrong person.

"I have a feeling that Dr. Wilder knows what he wants," she observed with some annoyance.

"I've been up all night and look like I've been dragged through a keyhole," I told her. "Do I have time to change first?"

"Well, he's been waiting almost a half-hour already. Do you think it's wise to keep him waiting any longer?" she asked.

It was a stupid question. Of course, it wasn't wise. It didn't matter what I looked like, what I was doing, or even if it was a mistake. If Jacob Wilder wanted to see me, then that was exactly what was going to happen, and it was going to happen immediately.

A clean white lab coat was a poor substitute for a shower and fresh change clothes, even if it was borrowed from a colleague, but it helped me feel a little better about my journey to the medical arts building. It was a strange alien land in which I found myself, much different than the corridors and waiting areas of the teaching hospital and clinic, which had become my home. The irony of my discomfort was not lost on me. I had been expecting it, if not dreading it for some time. But it wasn't supposed to happen today.

Stepping out of the elevator on the sixth floor, I stood facing the signage on the opposite wall. It left me stunned and feeling a little overwhelmed. There among the thirty-some physicians of the faculty practice was my name. In two days at noon, I would cease being a resident. At one minute past noon, I would become an attending physician at the teaching hospital and a member of the faculty.

As I stood there, the arm of an elderly gentleman wrapped around my shoulder and squeezed me firmly.

"Welcome," Dr. Wilder said.

Looking into my eyes, he smiled and said, "You know, you do sort of look like you've been dragged through a keyhole. Relax, you are going to do just fine."

Jacob Wilder was one of my first attending physicians when I was an intern. It seemed both so long ago and just the other day. Such was the paradox of time. I still felt that sense of awe in his presence. As interns we knew him as a world-renowned hematologist, a department leader, and a national expert in medical education. He was a giant. Watching him throughout the years, however, I came to know him as a most extraordinary physician. He practiced a medicine that wasn't described in any of the textbooks that I had studied.

He instilled in me a realization that we could be more than physicians; we could be healers.

"Come," Dr. Wilder said as he led me to an examination room. "I want you to meet someone."

Sitting in the corner of the room was an anxious appearing older man. His graying hair contrasted starkly with the dark tailored suit that he wore with a gold watch chain looped from his vest pocket. His erect posture gave him an almost regal appearance, one that seemed more at home in a corporate boardroom than in a physician's examination room. What struck me most about the man, however, was his pale complexion. His face was almost as white as his shirt.

"This is Mr. William House," my old attending said in introduction. "Mr. House, I want you to meet your new doctor."

Once again I stood in stunned silence, and to this day, I still can not remember all that was said in those first few minutes with Mr. House. Ten minutes later, or perhaps it was an hour, I sat with Dr. Wilder in his office. Like that inflicted by a dentist's Novocain, the numbness that I felt gradually dissolved to permit speech, albeit confused speech.

"Of all the doctors in this building," I said in disbelief, "and with all their expertise, why me?"

Leaning back in his desk chair, Dr. Wilder stared up

at the ceiling. He seemed to be in another place, and I wasn't sure he had heard my question. A broad smile grew slowly across his face, the kind nourished from a pleasant memory.

"I was just thinking about one of my teachers when I was an intern," he started. "We didn't have much back then. Diagnoses were difficult to come by, and when they did come, most of the time we couldn't do anything about them. Often, the only tool we had was the relationship we had built with our patients. It was powerful medicine, and it still is.

"My old professor always told me to treat each patient as if they were my last. Those words have never lost their power throughout the years. Every encounter was an opportunity to experience the perfection of life and to become better than we had been moments before. I heard those words again today, but the irony is that this is my last day seeing patients. I'm retiring from practice. Mr. House never should have been on my schedule, but there he was, my last patient, and yet another opportunity to explore the wonders that can only be found today."

"But why me, sir?" I asked again, emotion tightening my throat.

"It's not important for you to know why," he said staring directly into my eyes. "It's not important that we understand how people find us. It's only important that they have found us."

Two days later, shortly after the hour when my clinical privileges allowed, I sat with my first patient in the medical arts building. The laboratory studies that Dr. Wilder had ordered were clipped to his chart and among them was the answer for the pallor that I had noted earlier. He was severely anemic with a hemoglobin less than half of what was expected in a healthy man. The uric acid level in his bloodstream was high, as were some of the enzymes on his liver panel. I was most concerned, however, with his blood smear. More than half of his blood cells were immature forms. It could only mean one thing. William House had acute leukemia.

Despite an hour trying, Mr. House refused my efforts to admit him directly to the hospital. He noted that he had been ill for some time and that waiting an additional half-day would not make much difference. It was logic that was hard to dismiss, and he left the office to attend to important business before returning to the hospital the following morning.

Mr. House seemed unusually relaxed when I saw him the next morning in the hospital. He even laughed about finally having the time to read the morning newspaper. It wasn't the face that I was expecting to see, particularly from one who was about to embark on a long, difficult journey.

"Well, Mr. House," I said in surprise. "That trip home yesterday did you a lot of good. What did you do?"

He looked at me a little sheepishly.

"I went to the park," he said softly. "I had all of these things on my mind that I had to do. When I was halfway home, the car just seemed to steer itself to the park that I had used to go to with my wife. We went there every week when she was alive. I hadn't been back in years. She loved no place more, but I never saw the beauty that she saw—until last night. I sat on that same bench that we had sat on for more than thirty years. It overlooks the lake and the sunset. As I sat there, I realized that it might be my last sunset to watch, and all of a sudden, for the first time, I saw its beauty. I sat there for more than three hours, and it felt as though my wife sat there with me. This morning was the first since she passed that I didn't wake feeling alone."

Indeed, the days that followed were difficult for Mr. House, but we walked them together. He was one of my first patients, but for every visit I treated him as if it were our last. Mr. House lived to see many more sunsets, each of which he treated as if they were his last. Through the contemplation of the last of things came a special appreciation for the present. It was there we found the best of ourselves, our opportunity to serve, our understanding of life's meaning, and the potential to heal.

# Simple Steps for Putting the Eleventh Secret to Work

- Imagine that your best friend is moving far away tomorrow. What would you do with them today?

- You have a favorite hobby—working in the garden, painting, or perhaps watching birds. Imagine being told you could do it only one more time. What would that last time be like?

- Before your next encounter, pause a moment. Imagine that it will be your last. Decide that it will be your best.

When the oak is felled the whole forest echoes with its fall, but a hundred acorns are sown in silence by an unnoticed breeze.

—Thomas Carlyle

True silence is the rest of the mind; it is to the spirit what sleep is to the body, nourishment and refreshment.

—William Penn

*The Twelfth Secret*

# End Your
# Day in Silence

**T**HE piercing ring jolted me awake. It was not a refreshed wakefulness rather the feeling that I would have felt better had I not slept. It couldn't possibly be time to get up. I struggled to focus on the clock. It was 1:47 AM. I hadn't been in bed for more than two hours.

The day had gotten away from me. Mollie Jasper's early-morning respiratory failure had consumed much of my morning. By the time I had left the intensive care unit, the office schedule was beyond repair, even for Erin's creativity. My patients always seemed to understand emergencies, however, perhaps comforted by the knowledge that if their time ever came, I would be there for them as well. Still, there had been needs to be met, and keeping them waiting had made for a stressful day.

The evening had been sacrificed to a medical staff meeting—time spent not in the pursuit of knowledge but for the satisfaction of others. I had chaffed at the loss. After another hour spent with Mollie, I had made it home, too tired to do anything but tumble into bed.

The telephone rang a second time, and I stifled a groan when I realized Norman Seedwell was calling. He was a charming man, but among the legion of the worried well who I followed in my practice. While quite healthy, he seldom seemed to appreciate the gift that so many of my patients longed for.

"Doc, I can't sleep," he told me.

"I beg your pardon," I replied, convinced that in my drowsiness I had heard him wrong.

"I can't sleep," he repeated. "I've been trying for hours, but I just can't sleep."

"It's a problem both of us seem to be having, Mr. Seedwell," I said with an edge of sarcasm in my voice.

It was something that was unusual for me, and I immediately regretted having said it. Fortunately, he didn't seem to notice, too focused on his own problems.

"What can I do to help you, sir?" I asked in the calmest voice I could muster.

"Well, I don't know," he said in frustration. "Can't you call some medicine in for me?"

"Do you really want to go out in the middle of the night and wait at a twenty-four-hour pharmacy for sleeping pills that you won't be able to take until it's almost morning?" I asked him in disbelief. "Maybe this is something that we should talk about in the office."

"I guess you're right," he said. "This wasn't very well thought out."

Although it was something new for me to hear at night, several times every week, sometimes that many times in a single day, a patient sat in my office and complained about not being able to sleep. Medical school and residency had taught me to ask about their medications, the temperature of their bedroom, late-night eating, and their use of caffeine. On rare occasions cure could be found through the answers, but never healing.

For that, I had to ask special questions and more importantly, listen for the answers. They are questions that my teachers—my patients—had taught me. Now, when told about trouble sleeping, I ask my patient what they do before going to bed each night. Invariably, I am told, "I watch the late news on television." In those few minutes, my patients see graphic images of crime scenes. There are pictures of war. Talking heads discuss corruption and politics. Economists predict loss of jobs and recession. Video displays horrendous natural disasters and unbearable loss. Security experts predict terrorists in subways. And if we manage to survive it all, bird flu will wipe out mankind in the coming weeks. The news broadcast complete, we turn off the television and go to bed. I wonder why we can not sleep.

Like so often is the case in medicine, it is another example of the effects of energy on our lives. It is a self-inflicted disease, no less than those invited by years of smoking, poor diets, and lifestyles of abuse and excess. So, too, we choose the energy that we bring into our lives.

What we watch on television, listen to on the radio,

or read in the newspaper changes us in profound, if not subtle ways. It is energy that we invite into our lives, energy that soak into our beings, and energy that has the power to influence how we feel. The medical and popular literatures are filled with studies that demonstrate that watching violent movies and video games leads to aggressive behavior in adolescents and young adults. It is the effect of energy at work.

It is a realization that is empowering because once we recognize that we invite it into our lives, we can change it. Televisions have off switches. Radios have tuning knobs. Literature can replace newspapers. For those of us who choose to watch the late news, perhaps before retiring, we can surround ourselves with the higher energy of soft music, read passages of inspirational text, or sit in silence. Whether we call it reflection, meditation, or prayer, being alone with our thoughts is among the highest level of energy that we encounter. It, too, will change us.

Sometimes low-level energy comes to our lives not through invitation but through the journey we travel. Often, it is hard to avoid. Sometimes, it is our job not to avoid it. Such is the case with medicine. Early in medical school, a psychologist taught that an awareness of our feelings could help in a patient's diagnosis. Depressed patients often made us feel sad, while some personality disorders left us feeling angry and frustrated. What we were feeling, but were unaware of, was energy and how it could change us.

Sadness, frustration, and sometimes even anger are hard to avoid in medicine. Those with the desire to help will be exposed to, and influenced by, the energy of those seeking that help. The day's end often leaves physicians, nurses, and even technicians feeling bad, oblivious to how the energy about them has changed them.

When we can't change the energy around us, we can change how we react to that energy. I try to spend part of each day immersed in the healing energies that my teachers have shared with me. Being generous, aware and appreciative of the beauty and wonders around us, and in the service of others can restore peace to the most troubled day. It is in the silence that can be found at the end of the day, however, where we can find our greatest clarity, answers to our most troubling problems, and healing. But we can only give to others what have found for ourselves.

As I hung up the phone with Norman, I felt strangely appreciative. He was my teacher. Of all of the days when I needed that silence the most, it had somehow eluded me. But for the insomnia of a worried man, I might never have heard the silence that night, and in the silence, there was healing.

# Simple Steps for Putting the Twelfth Secret to Work

- Watch the first five minutes of the nightly news with a pencil and paper. Make a check for every story or video that depicts violence, reports bad news, instills fear, or makes you feel sad. Count up the checkmarks. Are you surprised by the total?

- For one week, do not watch the late news. Avoid movies and programming that have violent themes, exploit the troubles of others, or make you angry. Instead spend time with your family, work on a hobby, read a book, or listen to pleasant music. At the end of the week, look at yourself in the mirror. How do you feel? How have you slept?

- End your day in silence. Find a quiet and comfortable place where you won't be disturbed—resting in a favorite chair, sitting by the fireplace, or perhaps reclining on soft pillows on a floor in your home. Close your eyes. Take three deep abdominal breaths, exhaling through your nose, and then breath in a way that feels natural to you. Concentrate on the silence. Follow your thoughts wherever they may lead. Should they pause on troubles from the day, nudge them back to the silence and let go again.

Practice this for fifteen minutes each night or for as long as is comfortable. After one week, life will seem different.

- It takes three weeks to establish a habit. Make ending your day in silence a habit.